No More Bullying

Nancy Flowers

To: Ruthie,
Nancy Flowers

WinePress **Kids**

W.

To order additional copies of this title call:
1-877-421-READ (7323)
or please visit our Web site at
www.winepressbooks.com

If you enjoyed this quality custom-published book,
drop by our Web site for more books and information.

www.winepresspublishing.com
"Great books, defined."

WinePress Publishing (PO Box 428, Enumclaw, WA 98022) functions only as book publisher. As such, the ultimate design, content, editorial accuracy, and views expressed or implied in this work are those of the author.

ISBN 13: 978-1-60615-091-7
ISBN 10: 1-60615-091-X
Library of Congress Catalog Card Number: 2012904964

Printed in South Korea.

My name is Jacob. I'm a kid just like you.
Sometimes we kids don't know what to do.

So here's a story I hope will help you.
Please tell somebody when you're feeling blue.

Don't be a bully or be bullied either.
Both are not right to do.

I had a friend who was good and nice.
But he got bullied and then thought twice.

It hurt so bad he cried and cried.
He didn't know what to do.

He got so mad and then he thought,
I'll be the bully! Ah-ha—I'll show you!

He got real mean; no one knew why.
He never told about his hurt inside.

He hid his pain by lashing out.
And learned to be real cruel.

He yelled and screamed and waved his fists.
He looked like a silly fool.

He kept hurting others to ease his pain.
But his efforts failed and were all in vain.

Bad things can happen that are not right.
We're afraid to tell so we cry at night.

People can be mean in what they say and do.
We don't like when it happens to us—what about you?

Have you been hurt by others' words?
Or hurt others with your deeds?

No one likes to be made fun of; no one likes to be teased.
So if it happens, tell someone—will you stop it, please?

Don't be a bully or be bullied either.
Both are not right to do.

No one likes to be bullied, no one big or small.
Everyone's important—important one and all!

Parents/Guardians

Guide your children away from bullying with this story about Jacob and Josie, who teach that it's better to be kind than to be mean; and why it's just as important to let someone know if you are being bullied because "both are not right to do."

The second book in the "Tell Somebody" series, *No More Bullying* is designed to get children talking. When they find a safe place to share their fears, kids learn how to handle life's difficulties, allowing them to create healthy relationships.

With *No More Bullying*, your kids will not only avoid bullying, they will embrace new friends too.